Pre-Kindergarten Reading Readiness

Contents

Find the blocks with A and colour them **red**.

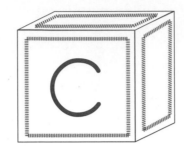

ASTRONAUT

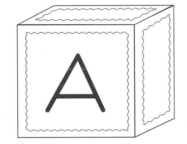

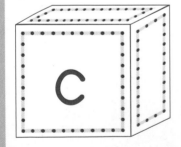

Find the blocks with **a** and colour them **brown**.

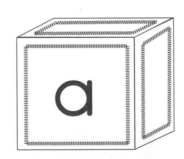

astronaut

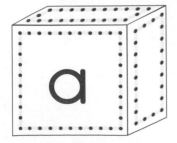

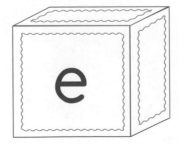

B Find the blocks with **B** and colour them **orange**.

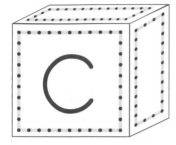  

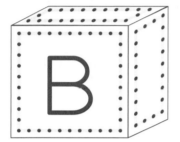 

BEAVER

---

b Find the blocks with **b** and colour them **blue**.

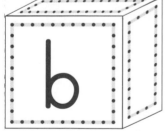 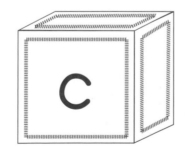 

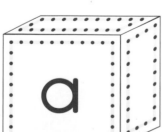 

beaver

3

C

Find the blocks with C and colour them **purple.**

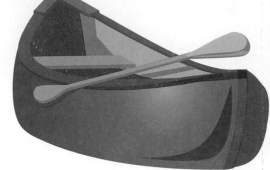

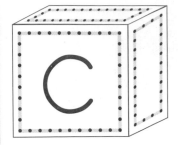 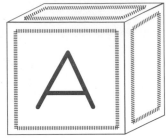

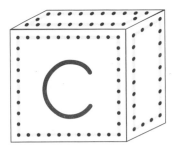 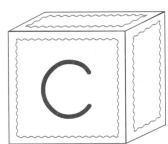

CANOE

---

c

Find the blocks with **c** and colour them **black.**

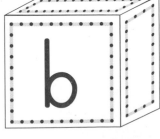 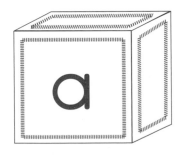

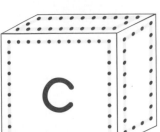 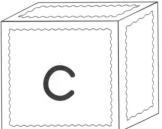

canoe

D

Find the blocks with D and colour them yellow.

DOLPHIN

d

Find the blocks with d and colour them green.

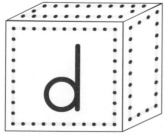
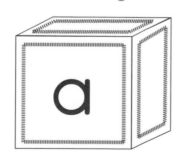

dolphin

E

Find the blocks with E and colour them **red**.

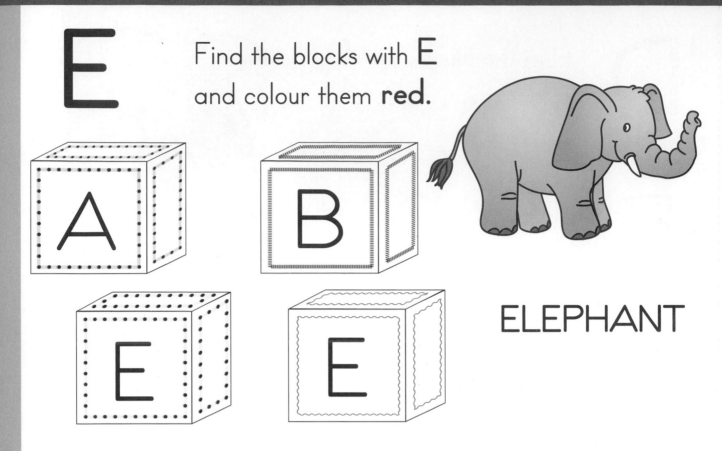

ELEPHANT

---

e

Find the blocks with **e** and colour them **brown**.

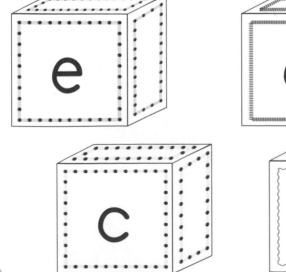

elephant

F

Find the blocks with F and colour them **blue.**

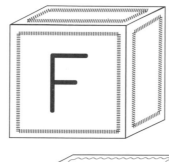
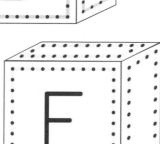
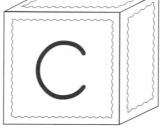

FLAG

f

Find the blocks with f and colour them **purple.**

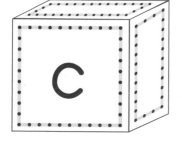

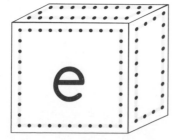

flag

7

G

Find the blocks with G and colour them **red**.

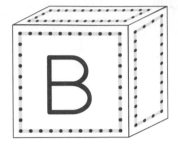 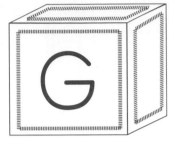

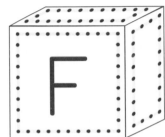 

GIRAFFE

g

Find the blocks with **g** and colour them orange.

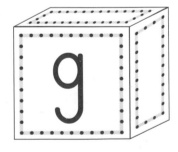 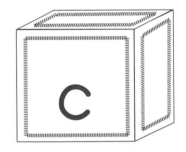

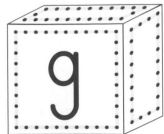 

giraffe

H

Find the blocks with **H** and colour them yellow.

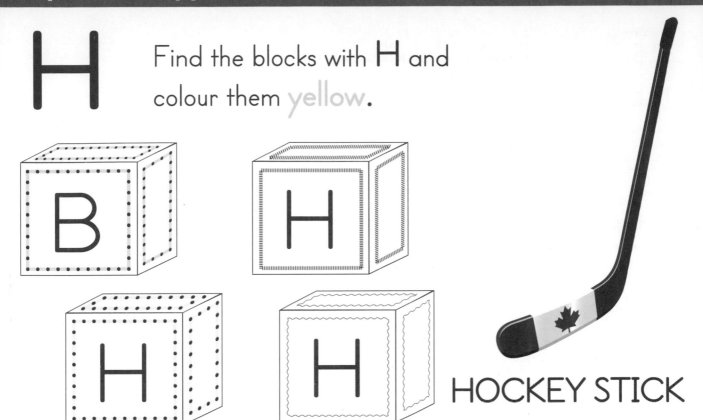

HOCKEY STICK

h

Find the blocks with **h** and colour them green.

hockey stick

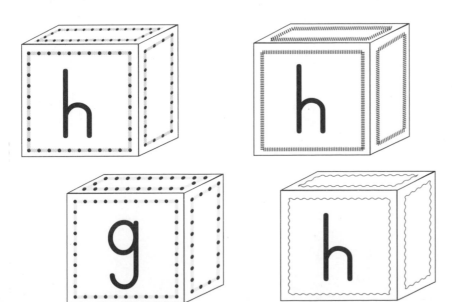

I

Find the blocks with **I** and colour them **red**.

G

I

I

H

IRON

i

Find the blocks with **i** and colour them **brown**.

i

i

g

h

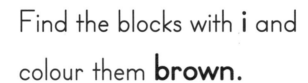

iron

J

Find the blocks with J and colour them **blue.**

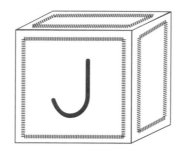

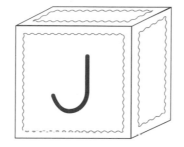

JELLY BEANS

j

Find the blocks with j and colour them **purple.**

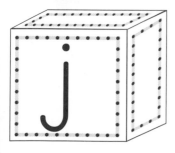
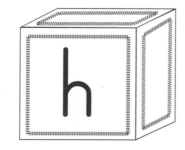

jelly beans

K

Find the blocks with K and colour them **black**.

KAYAK

---

k

Find the blocks with **k** and colour them orange.

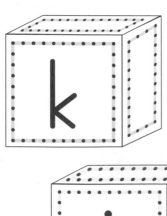

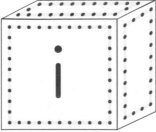

kayak

L Find the blocks with L and colour them **orange**.

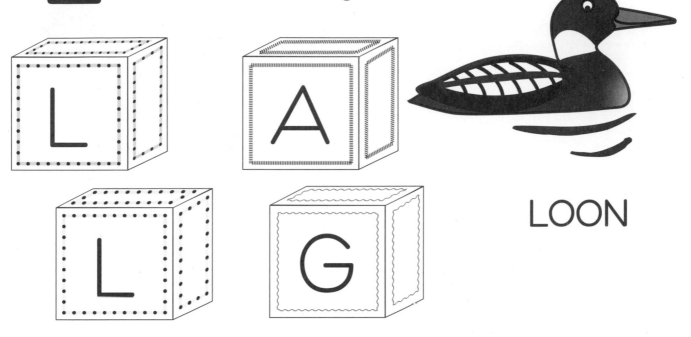

LOON

Find the blocks with I and colour them **blue**.

I

loon

M

Find the blocks with M and colour them **red**.

MOOSE

---

m

Find the blocks with m and colour them **brown**.

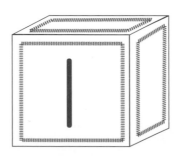

moose

N

Find the blocks with **N** and colour them **blue.**

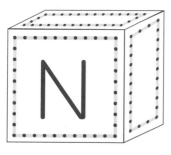

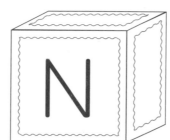

NEST

---

n

Find the blocks with **n** and colour them **purple.**

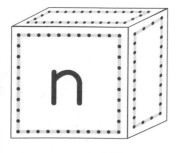

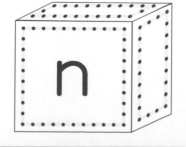

nest

O

Find the blocks with O
and colour them **black**.

OCTOPUS

Find the blocks with o

and colour them orange.

o

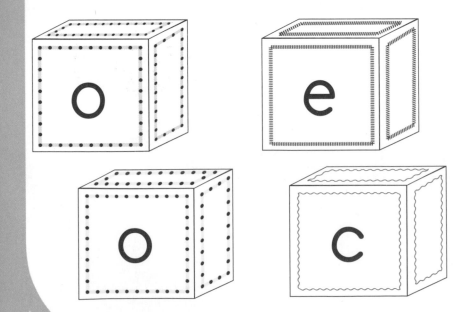

octopus

P

Find the blocks with P and colour them yellow.

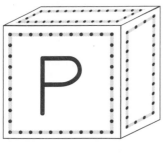

PUCK

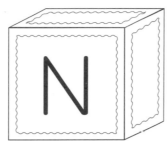

p

Find the blocks with p and colour them green.

puck

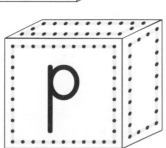

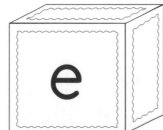

Q

Find the blocks with Q and colour them **red**.

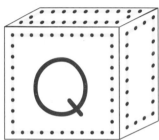

QUEEN

q

Find the blocks with q and colour them **brown**.

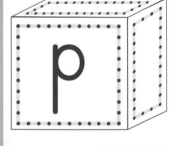
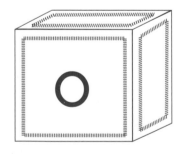
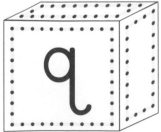

queen

R

Find the blocks with R and colour them **blue**.

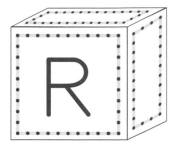
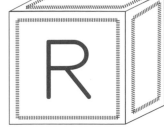

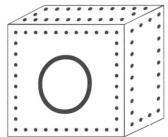

ROOSTER

r

Find the blocks with **r** and colour them **black**.

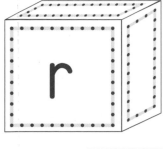
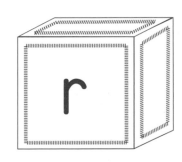

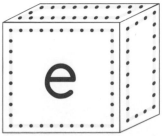
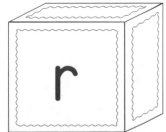

rooster

S

Find the blocks with S and colour them **purple.**

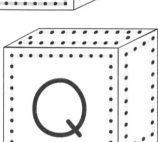

SCISSORS

---

s

Find the blocks with **s** and colour them **brown.**

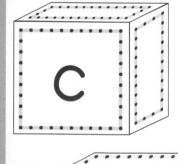

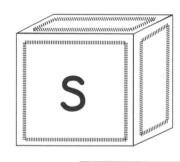

scissors

T

Find the blocks with T and colour them yellow.

TURTLE

t

Find the blocks with t and colour them green.

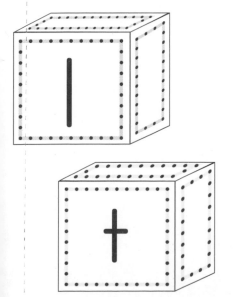

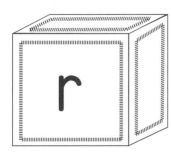

turtle

U

Find the blocks with U and colour them **red**.

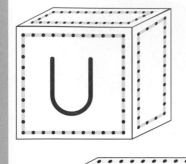
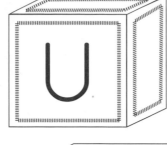

UMBRELLA

u

Find the blocks with **u** and colour them **brown**.

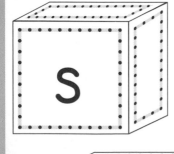
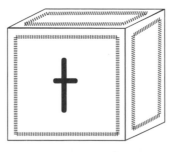

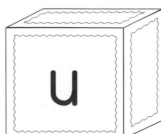

umbrella

22

V Find the blocks with V and colour them **blue.**

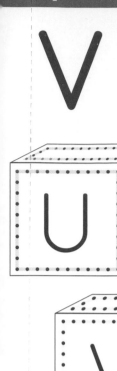
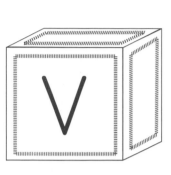
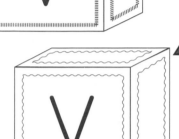

VOLCANO

Find the blocks with v and colour them **black.**

v

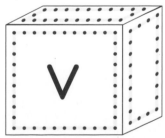
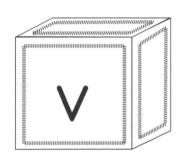

volcano

W

Find the blocks with W and colour them **purple**.

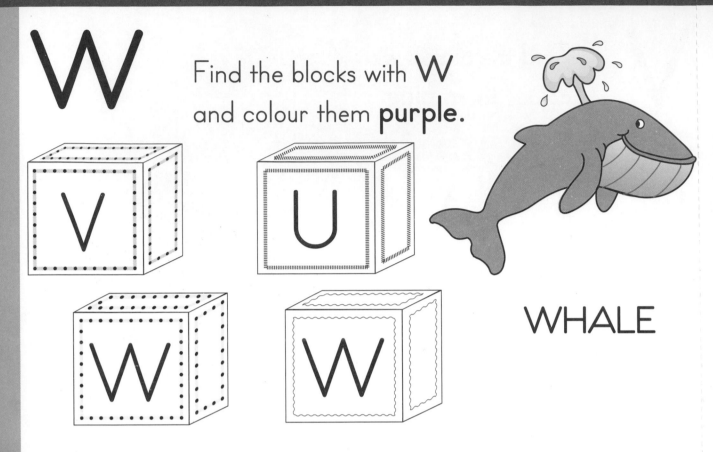

WHALE

Find the blocks with **w** and colour them **orange**.

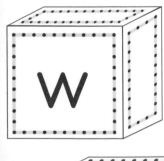

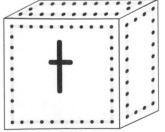

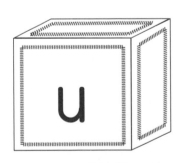

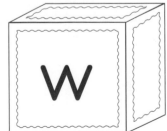

whale

Find the blocks with X and colour them yellow.

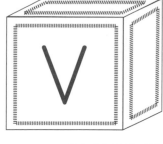
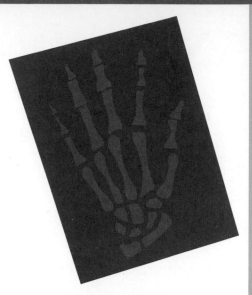

X-RAY

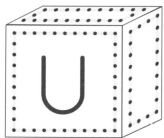

Find the blocks with x and colour them green.

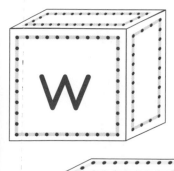

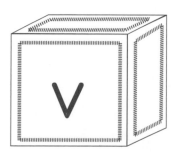

x-ray

25

Find the blocks with Y and colour them **red**.

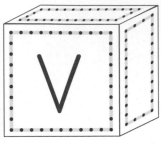
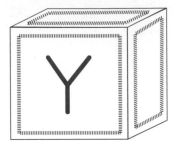

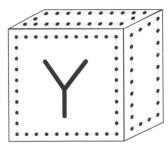

YO-YO

Find the blocks with y and colour them **brown**.

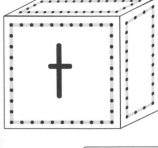
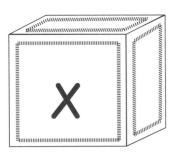

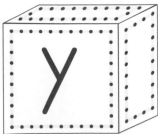

yo-yo

Z

Find the blocks with Z and colour them **blue.**

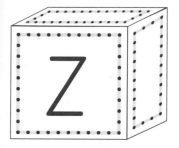
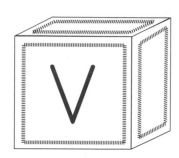
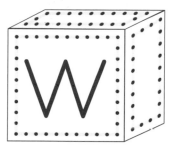

ZEBRA

---

z

Find the blocks with **z** and colour them **black.**

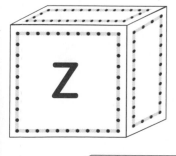
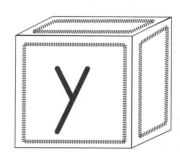
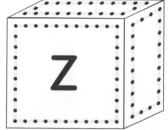

zebra

Aa

A is for astronaut.

Bb

B is for beaver.

Cc

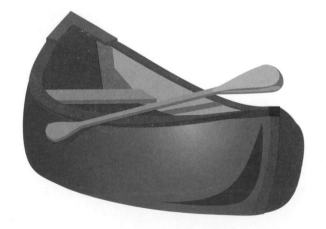

C is for canoe.

Dd

D is for dolphin.

Ee

E is for elephant.

Ff

F is for flag.

Gg

G is for giraffe.

Hh

H is for hockey stick.

Ii

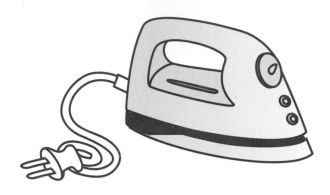

I is for iron.

Jj

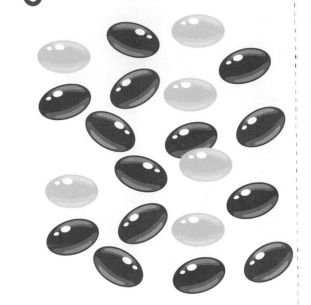

J is for jellybeans.

Kk

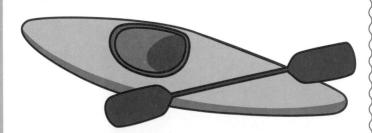

K is for kayak.

Ll

L is for loon.

Mm

M is for moose.

Nn

N is for nest.

Oo

O is for octopus.

Pp

P is for puck.

Qq

Q is for queen.

Rr

R is for rooster.

Ss

S is for scissors.

Tt

T is for turtle.

Uu

U is for umbrella.

V v

V is for volcano.

W w

W is for whale.

X x

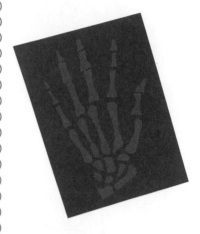

X is for x-ray.

Y y

Y is for yo-yo.

Z z

Z is for zebra.

a b c d e f g h i j k l m
n o p q r s t u v w x y z

Draw a line from the letter to the picture that starts with that sound. The first one is done for you.

c

e

h

r

m

d

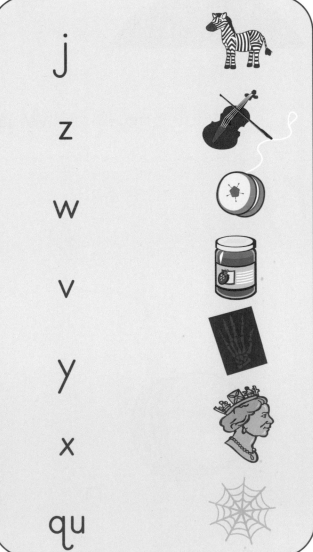

j

z

w

v

y

x

qu

a b c d e f g h i j k l m
n o p q r s t u v w x y z

Draw a line from the picture to the letter it starts with. The first one is done for you.

s
a
t
i
p
n

g
o
u
l
f
b
k

Words that rhyme **start** with **different sounds** and **end** with the **same sound.** Draw a line to each rhyming pair. One is done for you.

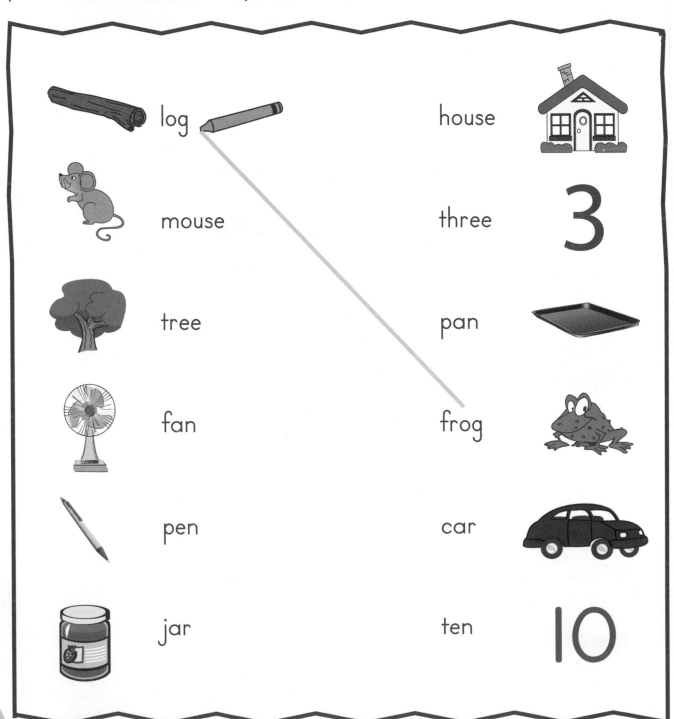

log   house

mouse   three

tree   pan

fan   frog

pen   car

jar   ten

Words that rhyme **start** with **different sounds** and
end with the **same sound.** Connect each rhyming pair
with a line. One is done for you.

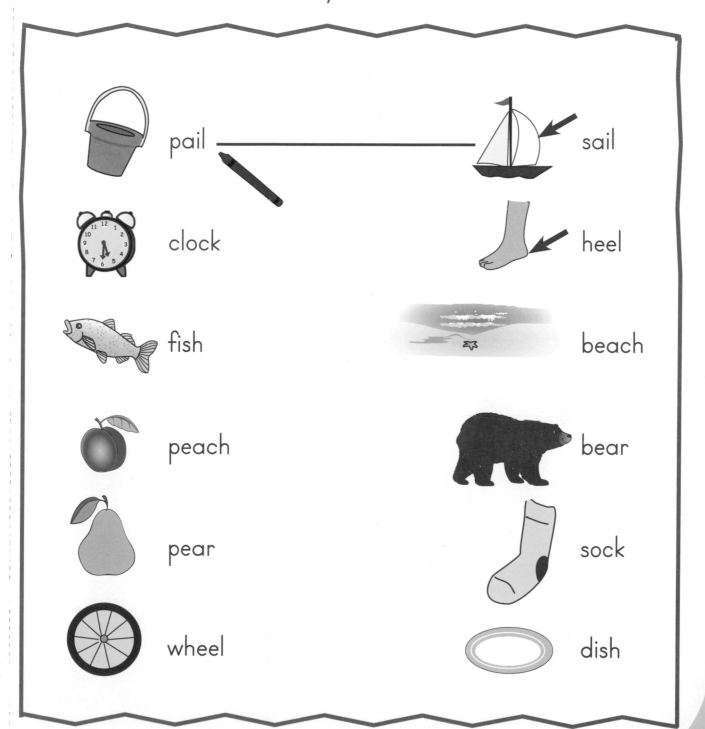

pail ——————— sail

clock   heel

fish   beach

peach   bear

pear   sock

wheel   dish

Words that rhyme **start** with **different sounds** and end with the **same sound**.

Look at the first picture in each row and say its name out loud. Circle the picture of the word that rhymes with it.

pen

pencil

ten

tire

fire

ant

dog

cat

frog

pail

tail

goldfish bowl

Read each sentence.
Draw a picture to show what it says.

I see the sun.

The boy can sail a boat.

Look at the brown cat.

The grapes are purple.

Look at the pictures that show what happened first and second. Then circle the picture that shows what happened third. Colour the pictures.

1

2

or

The Chipmunks' Cruise ™

by Janice Karman and Ross Bagdasarian

illustrated by Corny Cole
color by Dennis Durrell

Random House  New York

Copyright © 1984 by Bagdasarian Productions.
All rights reserved under International and Pan-American Copyright Conventions. Published in the United States by Random House, Inc., New York, and simultaneously in Canada by Random House of Canada Limited, Toronto.
Library of Congress Catalog Card Number: 83-62053   ISBN: 0-394-86385-2
Manufactured in the United States of America   1 2 3 4 5 6 7 8 9 0

THE CHIPMUNKS is a trademark of Bagdasarian Productions.

Dave Seville and the Chipmunks—Alvin, Simon, and Theodore—made their way along the deck of the S.S. *Lurleen* cruise liner.

"Welcome aboard, Mr. Seville," said the captain. "We're looking forward to seeing your boys perform tonight!"

Alvin grinned. "And I'm looking forward to seeing the ship!" he said.

"You can explore the ship after you've put your things away in the cabin," said Dave.

The ship pulled out of the harbor, and Dave led the way to their cabin.

Alvin put away his clothes very quickly—he left them in the suitcase and shoved the suitcase into a dresser drawer! Then he ran out ahead of the others to go exploring.

As Alvin raced down the deck he spotted something very strange. A woman was stuck in a porthole, kicking her legs frantically.

"Let me help you, ma'am," Alvin said politely. He tugged on her ankles. There was a loud sound of material tearing, and suddenly the woman popped free. She began to cry.

"Gee, I'm sorry your dress ripped," Alvin said to the woman. He looked at her torn sleeve and saw that she had a tattoo on her arm.

"I'm not crying about my dress," sobbed the woman. "It's my jewels. Someone stole them—and they're right there in cabin 209!" She pointed toward a porthole. Alvin peered in and saw sparkling jewelry on top of the dresser.

"I can't fit through the porthole," said the woman. She looked at Alvin. "But *you* can. Maybe *you* could get my jewelry for me!"

"Sure!" said Alvin.

The woman gave Alvin a boost into the cabin through the porthole. He picked up the jewels and passed them to the woman. Then he climbed out of the cabin.

"Thank you so much!" said the woman. She stuffed the jewelry in her purse and walked away.

"Boy, I'll have to tell Dave about this!" thought Alvin, and he ran off to find him.

He didn't look back—so he didn't see the woman take off her wig as she disappeared around the corner. She was really a man in disguise!

Alvin finally found Dave and his brothers back in the cabin.

"Listen to what happened to me, everybody!" he cried.

"I have something to tell *you*, Alvin," said Dave. "The captain and the ship's detective came by. They said there's been a theft aboard ship! Some jewelry was stolen from cabin 209."

Alvin gulped.

"Now, what's your news?" asked Dave.

"Uh—I can't remember," muttered Alvin nervously. He yawned. "Boy, I sure am tired. I think I'll take a nap."

Alvin climbed into the lower bunk and hid under the covers.

While Dave went to fix up the stage for that night's show, Simon and Theodore played detective. They went to cabin 209 armed with a magnifying glass and tweezers.

Simon pulled two hairs from the porthole and examined them under the magnifying glass.

"I know who our thief is!" he said.

"How do you know?" asked Theodore.

"Elementary, my dear Watson," Simon said. "These hairs are evidence. And just take a look at these fingerprints!"

"We know you're the thief!" Simon told Alvin a short time later. "Your fingerprints were all over cabin 209!"

"Not to mention the two chipmunk hairs we found on the porthole," said Theodore. "You're in big trouble!"

"Okay, okay, I did take the jewels," Alvin admitted. "But a lady tricked me into giving them to her. And the only thing I remember about her was a tattoo on her arm."

"Tattoo? Perfect!" said Simon. "A tattoo will let us identify her. And I think I know a way to trap her—right in our own cabin...."

Soon it was dinnertime. The three Chipmunks went to the dining room.

"Don't forget your lines," Simon whispered when they had almost finished eating.

"Boy," said Theodore loudly, "am I nervous about all those jewels in our cabin— CABIN 127."

The busboy looked at them. So did everyone else in the dining room.

"I wonder if it's safe to perform tonight and leave our cabin —CABIN 127— unguarded," said Alvin, also loudly.

"Let's get over to the stage and see how Dave is doing," Simon said.

But Dave was no longer at the stage. He had gone back to the cabin to pick up the Chipmunks for dinner.

"Hey, guys!" Dave called, opening the cabin door. "It's time for—whoops!"

Poor Dave! The Chipmunks had rigged a clever trap in their room to catch the jewel thief. In no time at all Dave found himself caught in a net that was strung from the cabin ceiling.

There was no way he could escape. All he could do was wait for someone to discover him. Soon he drifted off to sleep.

Meanwhile the Chipmunks were hard at work backstage.

"You're full of good ideas, Simon," said Theodore. He waved a paintbrush. "These cardboard figures we've made look just like us!"

"And with this record player hooked up, no one will know it's not us singing onstage," said Simon. "The thief will think it's safe to go into our cabin—and we can get away to check our trap!"

The Chipmunks were not the only hard workers that evening. The busboy was busy too. He had heard the Chipmunks talking at dinner. As soon as their concert began, he hurried to cabin 127 and began to search for jewels.

Only one drawer would not open—Alvin's! The busboy tugged and tugged.

"The Chipmunks' jewels *must* be in here," he muttered.

The Chipmunks' concert was soon going full blast. The captain and the detective were enjoying the show, although they did think the Chipmunks looked a little stiff.

Then the music's vibrations started to make the cardboard figures sway. The figure of Alvin tipped over and fell onto the record player! The Chipmunks' song began to repeat one line over and over.

"Something's wrong here!" said the detective. "Those aren't the Chipmunks! Come on—let's get over to their cabin!"

The busboy was still tugging at the drawer when the Chipmunks returned to their room. They peeked inside.

"That's our thief!" whispered Simon. "See the tattoo on his arm?"

Just then the drawer flew out of the dresser. Of course there were no jewels in it. There was only Alvin's suitcase!

The busboy fell backward from yanking so hard, and the Chipmunks rushed in and jumped on him.

"We've got the thief!" cried Theodore.

"Hold him down!" said Alvin.

The noise in the room woke Dave up.

"Mmff . . ." he groaned.

Simon looked up at the net. "If the guy down here is the thief," he said, "then who's *that*?"

"What's going on here?" called the captain, running into the room with the detective close behind.

"We rigged a trap to catch the thief—" Alvin began.

The detective and the captain looked up at the net. "Seville! So you've been caught red-handed!" said the detective.

"Excuse me, but the *real* thief is here," said Alvin. The Chipmunks stood up and revealed the busboy.

The detective and the captain pulled the busboy to his feet. As they did so, jewelry fell out of the man's uniform.

"Why—those are the jewels stolen from cabin 209!" said the detective.

The captain turned to Dave. "I'm very sorry, Mr. Seville. Mixups do happen. Nothing personal." He and the detective helped Dave get out of the net. Then they led the busboy away.

"What's going on here?" Dave asked.

"It's a long story, Dave," said Alvin. "It might take us the rest of the cruise to explain!"